THE OTHER CAST

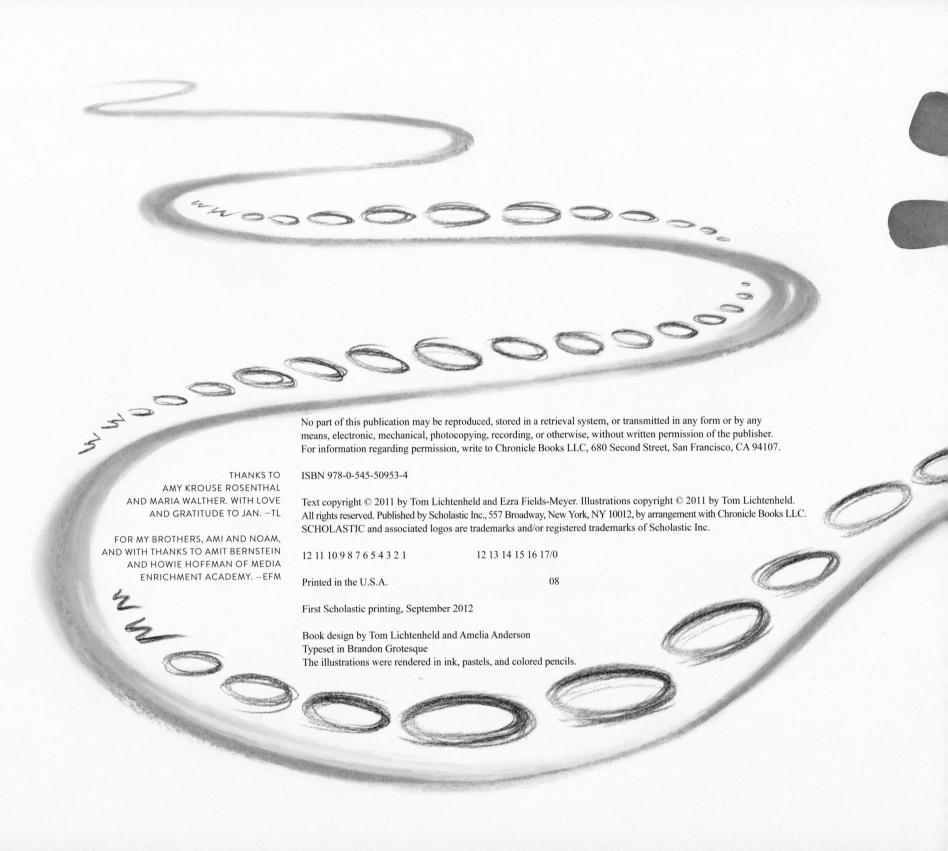

ISBN 978-0-545-50953-4

Text copyright © 2011 by Tom Lichtenheld and Ezra Fields-Meyer. Illustrations copyright © 2011 by Tom Lichtenheld. All rights reserved. Published by Scholastic Inc., 557 Broadway, New York, NY 10012, by arrangement with Chronicle Books LLC. SCHOLASTIC and associated logos are trademarks and/or registered trademarks of Scholastic Inc.

12 11 10 9 8 7 6 5 4 3 2 1   12 13 14 15 16 17/0

Printed in the U.S.A.   08

First Scholastic printing, September 2012

Book design by Tom Lichtenheld and Amelia Anderson
Typeset in Brandon Grotesque
The illustrations were rendered in ink, pastels, and colored pencils.

THANKS TO
AMY KROUSE ROSENTHAL
AND MARIA WALTHER. WITH LOVE
AND GRATITUDE TO JAN. —TL

FOR MY BROTHERS, AMI AND NOAM,
AND WITH THANKS TO AMIT BERNSTEIN
AND HOWIE HOFFMAN OF MEDIA
ENRICHMENT ACADEMY. —EFM

E-MERGENCY!

LOOK OUT FOR THE AUTHORS!!

AMBULANCE

SCHOLASTIC INC.

TOM LICHTENHELD

EZRA FIELDS-MEYER

ALL THE LETTERS LIVED
TOGETHER IN A BIG HOUSE.

HEY LOOK—
ALPHABET SOUP!

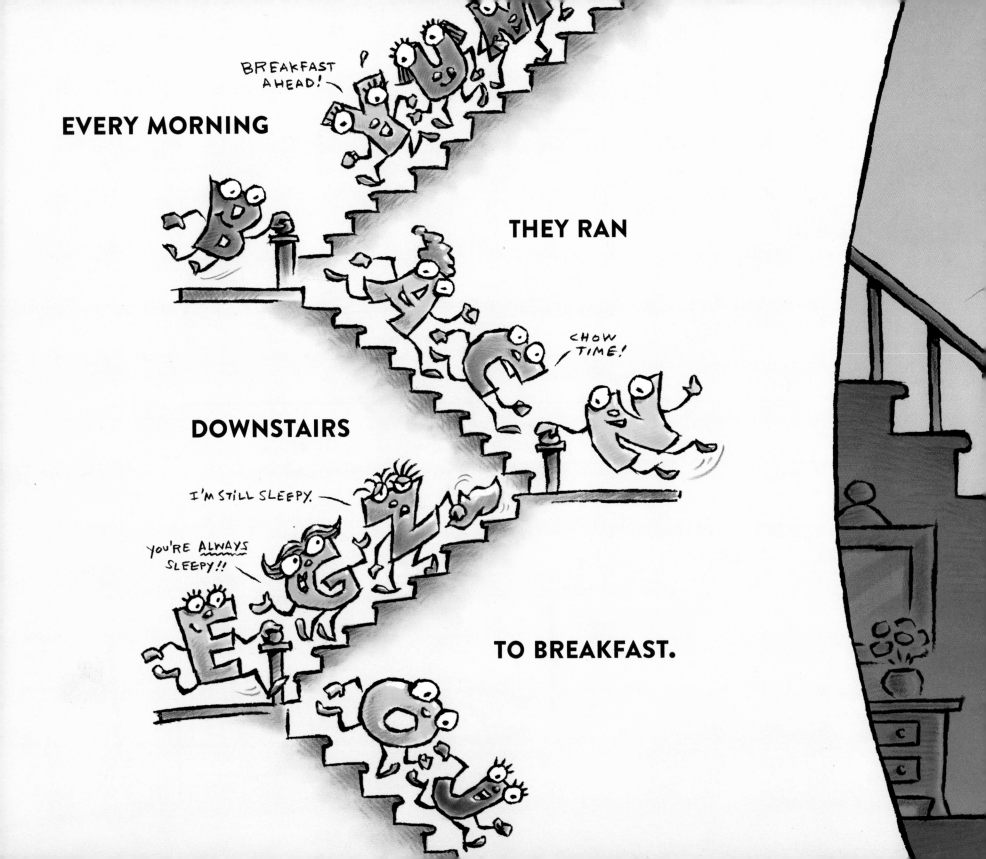

ONE MORNING, **E** CAME DOWN THE
STAIRS A LITTLE TOO FAST.

THE **EMT**S RUSHED IN WITH AN **IV**,

READY TO PERFORM **CPR**.

A AND **EXCLAMATION MARK** MADE THE BIG ANNOUNCEMENT.

AND THE REST OF THE LETTERS TALKED IT UP ON THE TALK SHOWS.

O DID HIS BEST FILLING IN FOR E,
BUT THE RESULTS WERE QUITE CONFUSING.

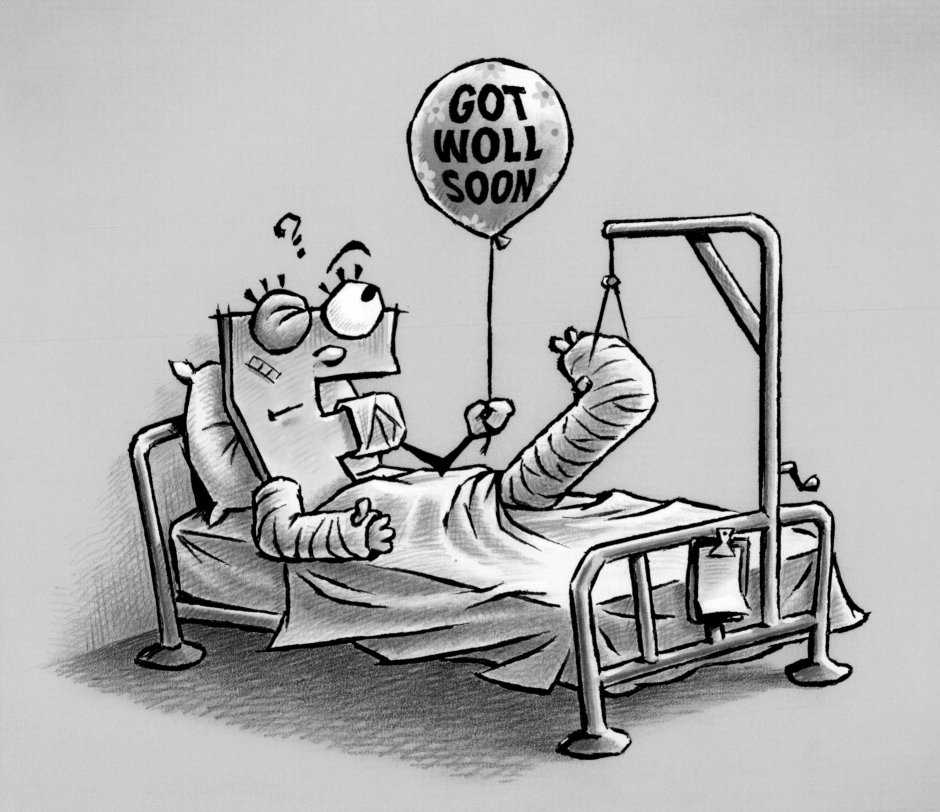

TO MAKE MATTERS WORSE, **E** WASN'T GETTING BETTER.
THE **MD**S COULDN'T FIGURE OUT WHY.

A DECIDED THEY NEEDED TO TAKE A TRIP TO SPREAD THE WORD ABOUT THE LETTER.

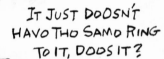

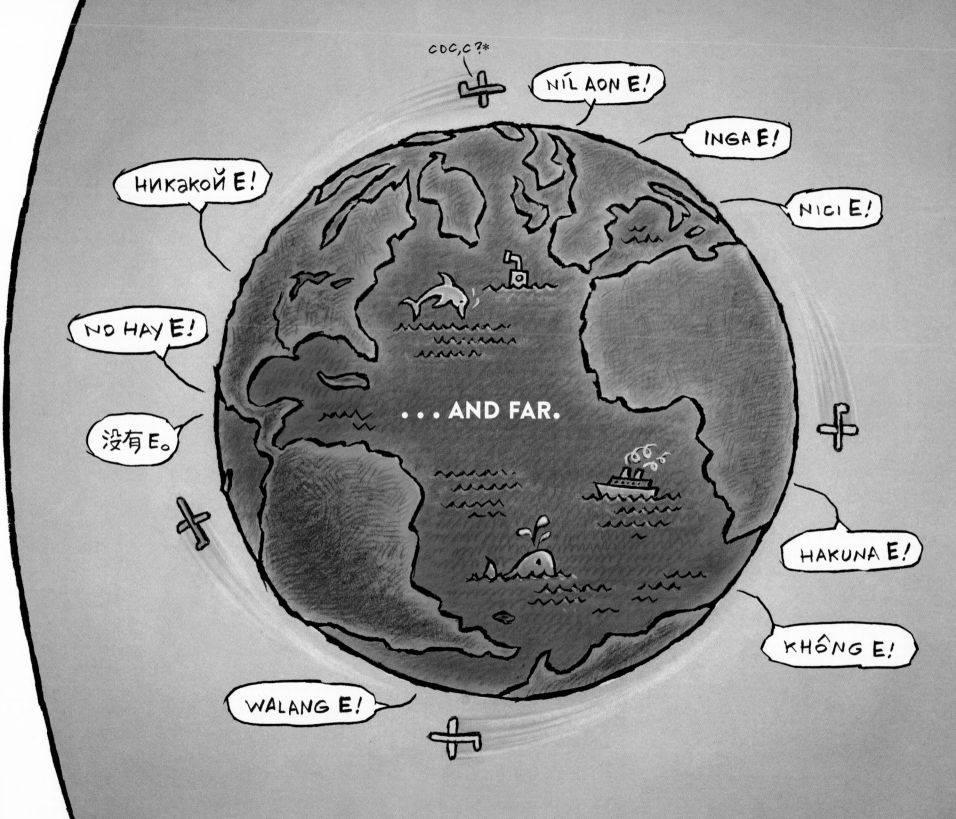

WHEN THEY GOT HOME, E STILL WASN'T RECOVERED.

THE LETTERS HAD A PROBLEM.

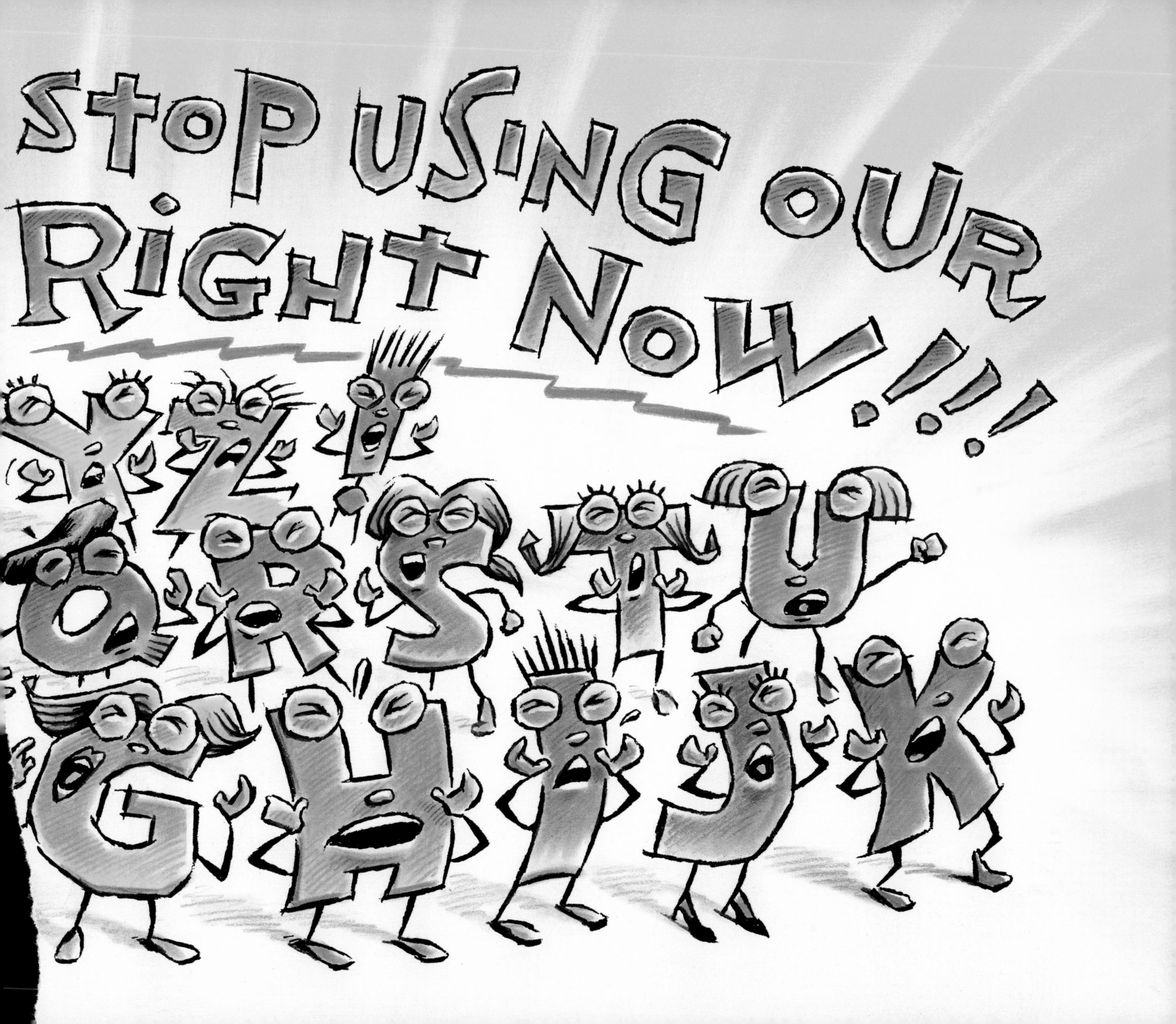
STOP USING OUR RIGHT NOW!!!

SO THO LAST PORSON USING YOU-KNOW-WHO STOPPOD.

QUICK AS A WINK, SHO
WAS OUT OF BOD AND ROADY
TO GO BACK TO WORK.

JUST IN TIMO FOR . . .

thE End.